Picture of me!

This super-pretty Hello Kitty Annual belongs to

....

Welcome!

Welcome to the Hello Kitty Annual 2015! Hello Kitty wants to share some of her favourite things with you. Get ready to have lots of fun with stories, puzzles, activities and much, much more!

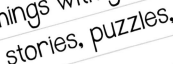

First published in the UK by HarperCollins *Children's Books* in 2014

1 3 5 7 9 10 8 6 4 2

ISBN: 978-0-00-755945-9

Written by Sarah Delmege

Designed by Emily Smyth

A CIP catalogue record for this title is available from the British Library.

Printed and bound in China

HarperCollins *Children's Books*

Contents

HELLO KITTY

Hello Kitty's family

Hello Kitty loves her family.
Here they all are.

Mimmy Mummy Daddy Hello Kitty Grandpa Grandma

Who is in your family? Draw or stick a picture of your family here.

Hello Kitty has lots of friends. She thinks they are all SUPER-SPECIAL!

Jody

Fifi

Tippy

Dear Daniel

Thomas

Timmy and Tammy

Hello Kitty's very best friend is her twin sister Mimmy. Who is your best friend? Draw or stick a picture of them here.

The super surprise

Hello Kitty woke up and stretched. The sun was shining through her curtains. It was going to be a beautiful day. Hello Kitty sat up in bed as a super-special thought popped into her head. She could have a picnic in the park that afternoon. How exciting!

Hello Kitty jumped out of bed and hurried to Mimmy's bedroom. She couldn't wait to tell her twin sister her idea – Mimmy loved picnics. Mimmy thought it was a super plan, but oh no! She remembered she had a flute lesson that afternoon. What a shame! Never mind, Hello Kitty could go ahead anyway.

Mummy was busy in the kitchen measuring out flour and butter. She smiled as Hello Kitty bounced excitedly into the room and explained her idea. But Mummy couldn't come – she had to cook some of her delicious cupcakes for a bake sale the next day. And Daddy had already started painting the garden fence, so he wouldn't be able to come either. Oh dear!

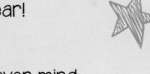

Never mind, thought Hello Kitty. She'd ring Fifi, Tammy and Dear Daniel and invite them to the picnic instead. An afternoon in the park with her friends would be so much fun.

Smiling to herself, Hello Kitty hurried over to the telephone. But nobody seemed to be at home. This was all going wrong!

Hello Kitty blinked back tears of disappointment. She had been so excited about the picnic. Oh well, it couldn't be helped. Hello Kitty put on her favourite music - that always cheered her up. But today the music didn't work - she still felt sad.

Hello Kitty picked up a book and started to read. Soon she was completely lost in the story and she didn't hear the doorbell ring or Mimmy, Mummy and Daddy all talking in hushed voices downstairs.

A little later Mummy called to Hello Kitty to come downstairs and try a cupcake. Hello Kitty put down her book and made her way downstairs. She looked around the kitchen; there was no one there and no sign of the cupcakes. Where was everyone?

Suddenly she caught sight of Mimmy waving at her from the garden. Then Hello Kitty's mouth dropped open in surprise as she saw Mummy, Daddy, Fifi, Dear Daniel and Tammy all grinning at her. And that wasn't all. Hello Kitty's eyes widened as she saw the most ENORMOUS picnic spread out on a pretty blanket. It looked fantastic!

Mimmy ran over and squeezed her sister's hand. She'd seen how disappointed Hello Kitty was about the picnic so she'd spoken to Mummy who said she could change her flute lesson.

Mummy said she'd bake her cupcakes later that evening. Daddy added that he was delighted to have a break from painting the fence and everybody laughed. Fifi, Tammy and Dear Daniel explained that they had been on their way to see Hello Kitty already when she was phoning them!

Hello Kitty couldn't believe that everyone had gone to so much trouble just for her. It made her feel so special. As she beamed at

her friends and family she felt like she could float away with happiness. What a super surprise! She was the luckiest girl in the world! And she had been right all along – it really was the perfect day for a picnic!

Farm fun!

There are five differences between these two pictures. Can you spot them all?

Colour in a bow each time you find a difference. Why not make each bow a different colour?

Picture 1

Picture 2

14

It's almost Christmas! What is Hello Kitty thinking about? Join the dots to find out, then colour in the whole picture!

15

Puzzle pieces

Hello Kitty is having lots of fun at the park with her friends. Can you find the right missing pieces to complete the jigsaw puzzle?

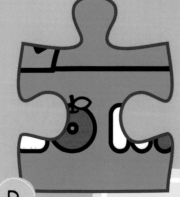

Write the number of the missing piece next to the correct puzzle piece.

Follow the trail of each bee to see which one has been gathering pollen from Hello Kitty's flowers.

Busy bee

Can you find the eight butterflies hiding on this page? Circle each one.

7

8

9

Hooray!
Go forward
one place.
10

11

SORRY!
Miss a go while
you spell Mimmy
backwards.
12

Race your friends around this
super-fun board game.

What to do:
- You will need a die and counters.
- Grab some paper and pens.
- Place your counters at the start.
- The youngest player goes first.
- Move around the board following
  the instructions.
- The first to the end is the winner!

13

SORRY!
Go back
one space.
14

15

Everyone wants
Hello Kitty's autograph
and sometimes it slows her
down! Practise your own
autograph. Miss a go while
you write it three times.
16

17

Swap places
with someone else
on the board.
You choose!
18

19

Talent spotter

Follow this fun flowchart and discover your special talent! Now ask your friends and family to find out theirs.

Start here!

Do you run everywhere?

Yes

No

Do you have lots of energy?

Yes

No

Do you love being outdoors?

Yes

No

Yes

No

Do you like making up stories?

Yes

Are you good at gymnastics?

No

Yes

Do you enjoy dressing up?

No

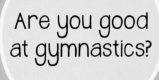

You're determined and active, like a sportsperson.

Do you love reading?

No

You're inventive, like a writer.

Yes

No

You're musical, like a pop star!

Do you sing along to the radio?

Yes

No

You're elegant and graceful, like a dancer.

Yes

Do you tap your foot to music?

You're flamboyant and creative, like a fashion designer.

Yes

The Christmas Show

·A HELLO KITTY STORY·

Hello Kitty was so excited. The cast of the school Christmas play was going to be announced, and she was hoping for a part. She gasped with excitement as she looked at the list on the notice board. There – next to the word 'soloist' in big bold letters – was her name!

Hello Kitty had been chosen to sing all by herself as part of the Christmas play. Wow! Dear Daniel, Fifi and Tammy rushed over to give Hello Kitty a big group hug. They were so proud of their friend.

That night, Hello Kitty went to bed feeling very happy. She was determined to be the best singer her school had ever heard. She closed her eyes and imagined herself singing on stage, dressed in a gorgeous sparkly outfit. It would be amazing!

Over the next few weeks Hello Kitty practised and practised. She hummed while she cleaned her teeth. She sang on her way to school and warbled all the way home again. Hello Kitty even asked Mimmy to film her so she could play back her performance and work out how to make it even better. She was going to be perfect.

Finally, the day of the school concert dawned, cold and grey. Hello Kitty woke with an uncomfortable feeling in her throat. She tried to call Mummy but nothing came out. Nothing at all! She had completely lost her voice.

Mummy popped her head round the door to see if Hello Kitty was awake. When she saw that Hello Kitty couldn't talk, she came over and told her to open her mouth wide and say "ahh". Hello Kitty tried, but nothing happened. Mummy gave Hello Kitty a kiss and explained gently that there was no way she'd be able to sing that night. Oh no!

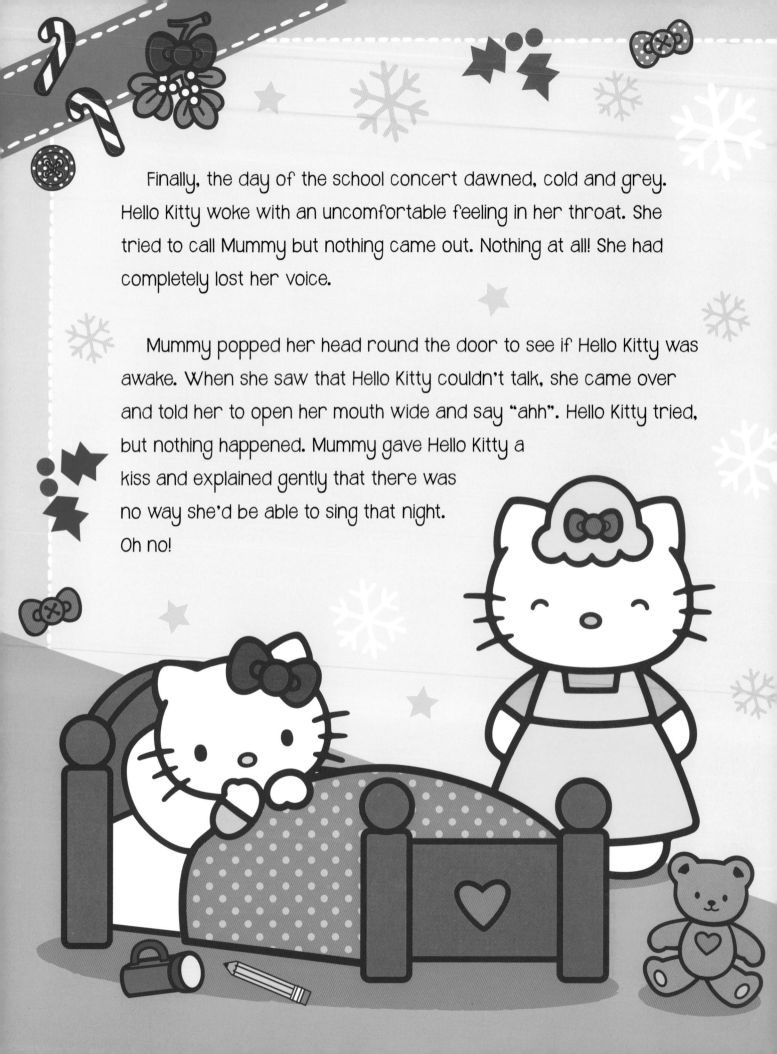

Poor Hello Kitty! Mimmy knew how upset Hello Kitty must be. She wished there was something she could do to make her sister feel better, especially after she'd practised so hard. Suddenly an idea popped into her head.

Mimmy felt her tummy flutter with excitement.

Later that night, Hello Kitty made her way into the school hall with Mummy and Daddy. It had started to snow and it felt so Christmassy! Hello Kitty felt really sad that she couldn't take part in the show but tried to smile; she didn't want to ruin it for anyone else. Dear Daniel, Fifi and Tammy peered round the curtain and grinned at her. Hello Kitty took a deep breath and waved back at her friends.

The show went brilliantly. Hello Kitty made sure to clap extra loudly. Then it came to the soloist slot. Fifi stepped forward and explained that as Hello Kitty had lost her voice and wasn't able to perform, they had a special surprise for everyone. Hello Kitty was puzzled. What could it be?

A giant screen slowly lowered on to the stage. The lights went out, the screen flickered and then an image of Hello Kitty standing in her bedroom appeared on the screen. Hello Kitty gasped as she realised it was a film of her practising her performance at home. She sounded really good! It was like a super-cool pop video.

As the song ended, there was a moment's silence, then the whole room burst into huge applause. Suddenly a bright spotlight picked out Hello Kitty in the audience and her teacher, Miss Davey, told her to stand up and take a bow. Hello Kitty went bright pink as everyone cheered even louder.

After the show Mimmy explained that Dear Daniel had helped her put a film together from all the videos she had taken over the last few weeks. And Miss Davey had thought it was a brilliant idea to play it at the concert. Hello Kitty beamed. She felt like the luckiest girl in the world. What a super Christmas surprise.

Seek and find

Help Hello Kitty to tidy her bedroom and find her favourite things.

Put a tick in the box next to each item when you spot it.

An orange hat ☐

A stylish bag ☐

A pink bow ☐

A pair of cowboy boots ☐

A necklace ☐

A crown ☐

A cup of tea ☐

Pink nail varnish ☐

A clock ☐

A pink comb ☐

HELLO KITTY

cookery code

What are Hello Kitty and her family going to cook? Find each item from the grid below in the larger picture, then copy the letter nearby to spell out the answer.

s
Flour
n
p
c
Butter
a
a
e
k

Answer grid

☐ ☐ ☐ ☐ ☐ ☐ ☐ ☐

Cute colouring

Hello Kitty and her friends are having lots of fun dressing up as cute animals. Use the colour key to help you finish the picture.

1 2 3 4

5 6 7 8

31

Odd one out

Hello Kitty and her sister Mimmy have the same of everything - except for one item. Can you find it?

33

Seasonal search

Hello Kitty loves all the seasons: blossom in spring, sunshine in summer, falling leaves in autumn and snow in winter. Can you help her to find the seasonal words in each grid?

SPRING

```
g  s  f  r  t  a  b
h  a  l  a  m  b  u
r  d  o  n  m  u  d
i  m  w  z  z  h  s
e  n  e  y  t  n  u
c  b  r  d  v  z  b
b  l  o  s  s  o  m
```

blossom · flower · buds · lamb

SUMMER

```
i  s  t  n  v  c  b
t  h  v  z  u  s  i
a  o  b  e  a  c  h
h  r  n  x  s  b  n
l  t  q  f  h  a  t
u  s  n  s  c  b  f
o  h  o  t  m  t  n
```

hot · beach · shorts · hat

AUTUMN

```
z  i  m  n  z  z  a
w  i  n  d  y  t  c
v  c  b  t  d  v  o
u  a  y  y  x  n  r
p  u  m  p  k  i  n
s  b  n  l  r  v  f
h  a  r  v  e  s  t
```

acorn · pumpkin · windy · harvest

WINTER

```
s  n  o  w  m  a  n
l  a  t  a  h  t  n
e  s  b  n  i  r  q
d  k  g  z  c  t  n
g  l  o  v  e  s  i
e  m  i  n  g  z  v
l  n  z  b  t  s  c
```

snowman · ice · sledge · gloves

34

Help Hello Kitty put these pretty balloons in order of size. Number the boxes from 1 to 5 starting with the biggest first.

Make your room every little bit as stylish as Hello Kitty's with these pretty door signs.

Hello Kitty

shhh! I'm sleeping!

Sanrio
LICENSE
©'76, '14 SANRIO CO., LTD

What to do:

When you've finished reading your Annual, cut out these pages and stick them on to card. (If you don't want to cut up your Annual, then copy or photocopy these pages.) Then, cut out along the dotted lines, stick the two halves back to back and hang it over your door handle.

ASK AN ADULT TO HELP WITH CUTTING OUT!

I'm AWAKE! Come on in!

Hello Kitty

Sanrio
LICENSE
©'76, '14 SANRIO CO., LTD

Weather report

Hello Kitty is pretending to be a weather reporter. Can you report on what the weather's been like near you by drawing the correct symbols in the 'Yesterday' and 'Today' spaces? What do you think the weather will be like tomorrow? Draw your answers in the 'Tomorrow' space.

Today:

Yesterday:

Tomorrow:

sun   rain   snow   cloud   wind   lightning

Hello Kitty loves the colour pink. Draw as many pink things as you can think of in the space below.

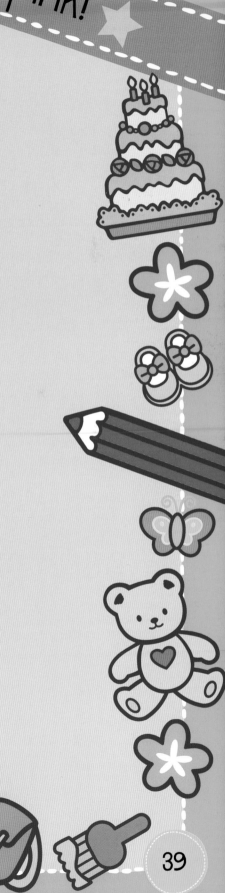

The perfect present

Dear Daniel's birthday was getting close and Hello Kitty wanted to get him the perfect present. She felt excited just thinking about it. Hello Kitty loved giving presents. In fact, she loved everything about birthdays!

Dear Daniel likes:

 ⭐ Photography

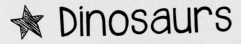 ⭐ Dinosaurs

 ⭐ Football

Hello Kitty thought hard. What should she get Dear Daniel? Grabbing her most sparkly pen and a piece of pink paper, Hello Kitty wrote a list of all the things she knew that he liked.

Hello Kitty decided to call Fifi, Timmy and Tammy and check what they were getting for Dear Daniel. Imagine if they all gave him the same thing!

Fifi said she had already got Dear Daniel a new football and Tammy excitedly explained that she had seen a brilliant book packed with pictures of dinosaurs that she knew Dear Daniel was going to love. Timmy said he had found a lovely strap for Dear Daniel's camera.

Oh dear. Hello Kitty stared at her list. It sounded as if Fifi, Timmy and Tammy had all of Dear Daniel's favourite things covered already. The birthday was only two days away and Hello Kitty had no more gift ideas. Whatever was she going to do?

There must be something else she could give Dear Daniel that he would like. She thought hard about all the things she loved about birthdays...

★ Cake
★ Parties
★ Singing
★ Presents

Suddenly a super-special idea popped into Hello Kitty's head. She knew the perfect thing for Dear Daniel – whyever had she not thought of it before? Hello Kitty beamed with excitement – this was going to be fun!

Hello Kitty quickly explained her idea to Timmy, Tammy and Fifi. She suggested that they throw Dear Daniel a surprise party at Hello Kitty's house. They could have a cake in the shape of a dinosaur and Daddy could let Dear Daniel use his special camera to take pictures of all the fun! Part of the afternoon could also be a football tournament in the garden. The friends gasped in delight. This idea had all of Dear Daniel's favourite things rolled into one. How exciting!

There was a lot to organize. Hello Kitty wrote a list of everything they needed and the friends got busy making dinosaur and football bunting. Then it was time to decorate the cake. Hello Kitty, Fifi and Tammy had great fun mixing all the gooey icing to decorate it. It looked yummy.

Daddy helped the excited friends hang up the bunting. By the time they'd finished, the room had been transformed. Footballs and dinosaurs hung from every corner. Hello Kitty hugged herself with happiness; she couldn't wait for Dear Daniel to see it.

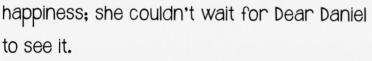

The next day was Dear Daniel's birthday. Hello Kitty rang him early in the morning to wish him a happy birthday and ask him to pop round that afternoon at four o'clock to pick up his present. She had to try very hard not to giggle down the phone. Dear Daniel was going to be so surprised!

That afternoon, the friends gathered excitedly in the house. DING DONG! The doorbell rang. Hello Kitty winked at everyone and put her finger to her lips before going to answer the door. Hello Kitty managed to keep a straight face as she told Dear Daniel to go into the house where his present was waiting. Dear Daniel went pink with delight as everyone clapped and cheered and shouted SURPRISE! Hello Kitty jumped for joy. She really had thought of the perfect present.

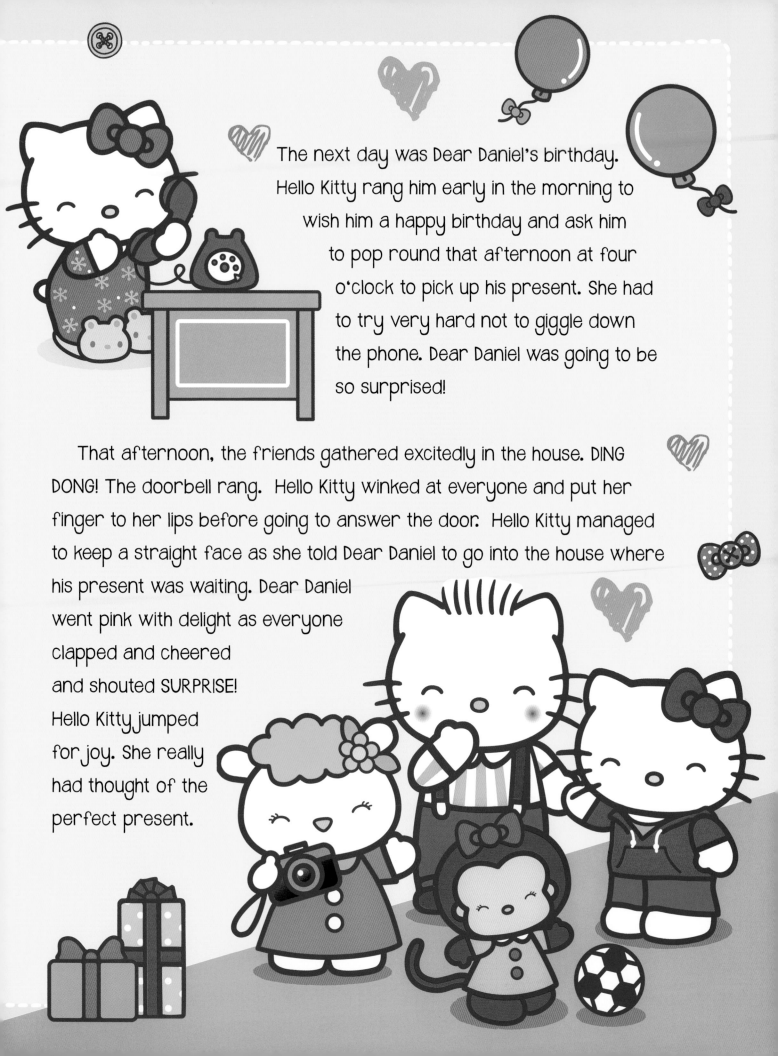

Quirky quiz

What can you remember about the story? See how many of these questions you can answer!

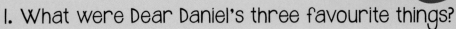

1. What were Dear Daniel's three favourite things?

2. What was the cake made in the shape of?

3. Where was the party held?

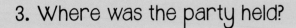

4. What was Dear Daniel going to use to take photos?

5. What kind of decorations did the friends make?

.... got

(Your name here)

.... questions right!

HELLO KITTY

Park fun

Hello Kitty is having fun playing outside with her friends. But oh dear - their kites have got tangled.

Kite tangle

Trace the kite tails to find out which kite belongs to which friend.

Fifi

Jody

Tippy

Hello Kitty

Dear Daniel

Word game

There are lots of things to spot in the park. Here are three, but the letters are all mixed up. Help Hello Kitty to solve them.

c k
d u
_ _ _ _

o n
p d
_ _ _ _

t r
e e
_ _ _ _

Duck twins

There are lots of ducks on the park pond. Can you spot which one is the exact match for the duck in the frame?

Spottery lottery

Play this super-fun game on your own or with friends next time you're out and about!

Use a pencil so you can play this game again and again!

Card 1

☐ Blue car

☐ Umbrella

☐ House

☐ Bird

Card 2

☐ Bench

☐ Ball

☐ Bus

☐ Bicycle

What to do:

Take this game with you next time you're on a car, train or bus journey.

If you're playing alone:
- Choose a card.
- When you see an item on the card, tick the box next to it.
- Then see how long it takes you to spot all the items on that card.

If you're playing with friends:
- Choose a card each.
- When you see an item on the card, tick the box next to it.
- The first person to spot all the items on their card is the winner!

Card 3

Hat

White car

Cow

BUS STOP

Bus stop

Card 4

Sheep

Scooter

Red car

Boat

Hello Kitty loves Teddy

Hello Kitty loves Teddy. She takes him with her everywhere she goes. What's your favourite toy? Draw it in the space below.

Shadow fun

Can you help Hello Kitty to match the teddies to the shadow shapes? Draw lines to match them.

Teddy match-up

Can you find the shadow that matches Hello Kitty's favourite toy?

A

B

C

D

E

53

Milkshake maze

Can you get Hello Kitty to her seat at the table? See how many milkshakes you can collect along the way!

The Hello Kitty Milkshake Shop

START →

→ FINISH

Get ready to have some super story fun with Hello Kitty. Whenever you reach a picture shout out what it shows. There's a grid at the bottom of the page to help you. And every time you see any **BIG WORDS** you need to act them out.

The fancy dress party

is super-excited. She's going to a fancy dress party and there is a for the best outfit.

What should wear? Luckily she has lots of fancy dress outfits to try on. She pulls out her fancy dress , opens it up and looks inside.

Wherever should she start?

Hello Kitty

box

prize

First Hello Kitty pulls a outfit out of the box. She tries to make a sound like a 🦁. **ROAR!** Oh dear, 🐱 doesn't sound loud enough to be a 🦁.

Next, 🐱 pulls a 🐸 outfit out of the 📦. She tries it on. She tries **JUMPING** like a frog and makes some 🐸 noises. **RIBBIT RIBBIT.** 🐱 doesn't think she can **JUMP** well enough to be a 🐸.

Hello Kitty reaches back into the 📦 and pulls out a 🐝 outfit. She wriggles into it. She makes a **BUZZ** noise and **FLAPS HER ARMS** pretending to fly. 🐱 doesn't think she can **BUZZ** well enough to be a 🐝.

Hello Kitty

lion

frog

Suddenly  has a super idea! She knows what the perfect outfit would be. reaches back into the and pulls out a beautiful, sparkly, outfit.

tries it on. She **SPINS** round three times in front of the mirror. It's perfect. can't wait to go to the fancy dress party. She **WAVES** her three times and wishes that all of her friends have a wonderful time at the party.

Can you make a wish with Hello Kitty?
Close your eyes and make it now.

box

bee

fairy

wand

Where's Hello Kitty?

Hello Kitty is such a superstar that everyone tries to look like her. Can you find the real Hello Kitty?

This is the real Hello Kitty. Find her in the crowd.

Can you spot these other things? Draw a circle round them when you see them.

Fun things!

What to do:

Close your eyes and put your finger on the page to find out which activity you should do!

Hello Kitty is never bored with this super-fun boredom buster.

Invent a new dance.

Read this Annual again from the beginning.

Learn a new word.

Read a book.

Make a butterfly painting.

Sing your favourite song backwards.

Goodbye

This is to certify that

Add your name →

....

has had lots of Official Annual fun with Hello Kitty.

I have:

Coloured in costumes ☐
Read fun stories ☐
Made a cute door hanger ☐
Played a Hello Kitty board game ☐

Now circle the words that sum up this book

super-fun   brilliant

cute

pretty   fabulous

What was your favourite
thing in this book?
Why not go back
and do it again?

2015

HELLO KITTY

Page 14

Page 16

1 : C   2 : E   3 : B

Page 17

Page 28

Page 29

Page 32-33

The item is a teddy bear

Page 34

Page 35

Page 46

1. Photography, dinosaurs and football
2. A dinosaur
3. At Hello Kitty's house
4. Daddy's special camera
5. Dinosaur and football bunting

Page 47

Hello Kitty is dreaming
about the colour: pink

Page 48

Page 49

duck   pond   tree

Page 52

Page 53

Teddy D

Page 58